GARFIELD
IN THE ROUGH

BY: JIM DAVIS

ℛ ℛ
Ravette London

This edition first published by Ravette Limited 1987.

Printed and bound for Ravette Limited,
3 Glenside Estate, Star Road,
Partridge Green, Horsham,
Sussex RH13 8RA
by Mateu Cromo Artes Gráfica, s.a.

ISBN: 0-948456-47-7

GARFIELD
IN THE ROUGH

Campers own bed . . . to insure that no roots, rocks, sticks, or stems interfere with a good weekend's sleep.

Headphone set – to tune out those distracting sounds of nature.

Gas grill – for barbecuing small woodland creatures that forage too close to the camp site.

Pocket coffee maker – this compact morning eye-opener is also wash 'n' wear.

Pocket blender – for blending roots, herbs, and berries with your favourite ice cream.

Electric can opener – a must for the campers who can't hunt, fish, or trap.

Colour TV – for tuning in old Tarzan movies to enhance the camping experience.

50 lb. bag of kitty litter – no fuss, no mess – sanitized and completely biodegradable.

Fully stocked refrigerator – camping is always more fun when you take your best friend.

Garlic clove talisman – to ensure the campers "King of the Hill" superiority in the food chain cycle.

Microwave oven – plus 200 miles of extension cord.

Credit cards – for the motel in case the weather is anything but perfect.

Telephone – camper can constantly stay in touch with his agent, lawyer, accountant, broker, pizzeria, and suicide prevention hotline.

Inflatable easy chair.

AM/FM cassette forest blaster – to assist the New Wave camper in break dancing across the forest floor.

CAMPING SUPPLY GUIDE

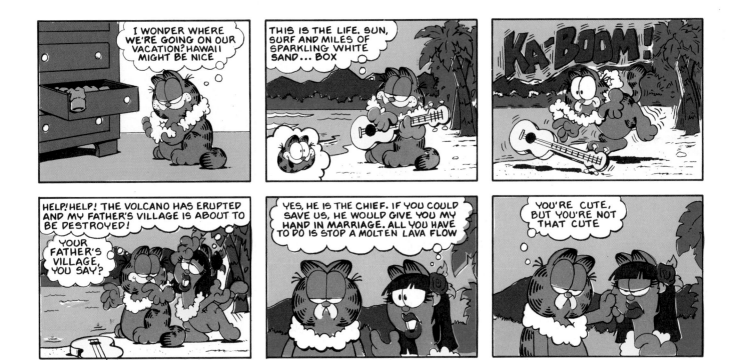

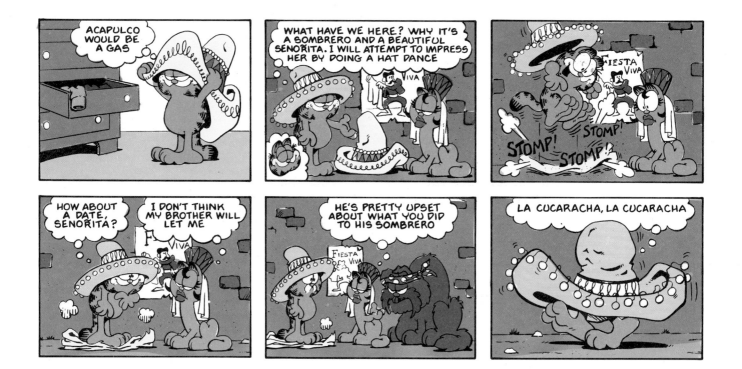

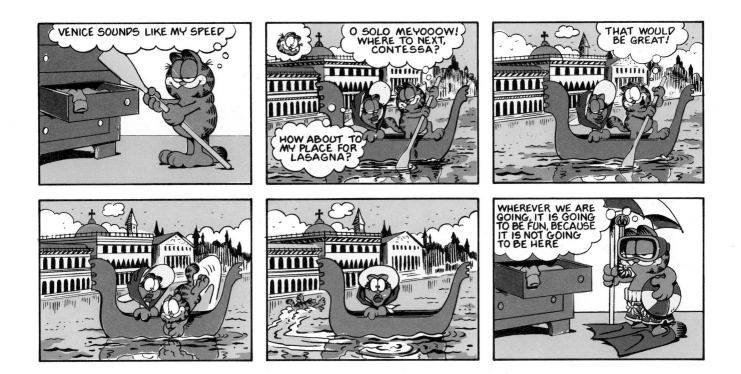

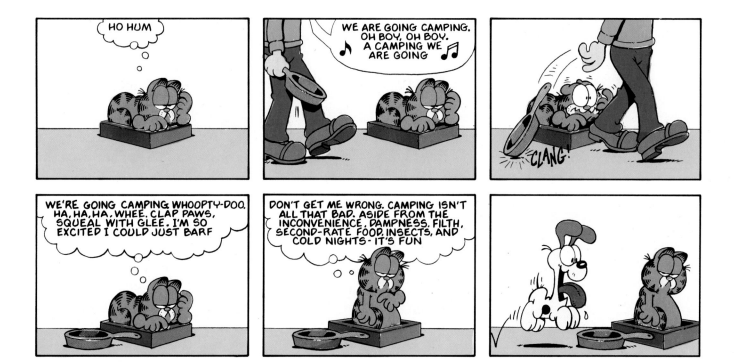

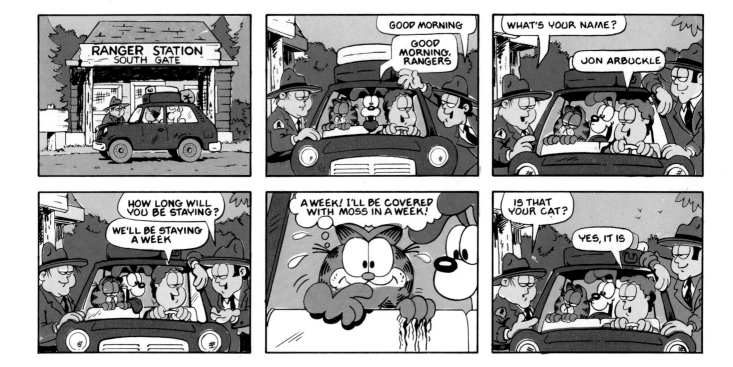

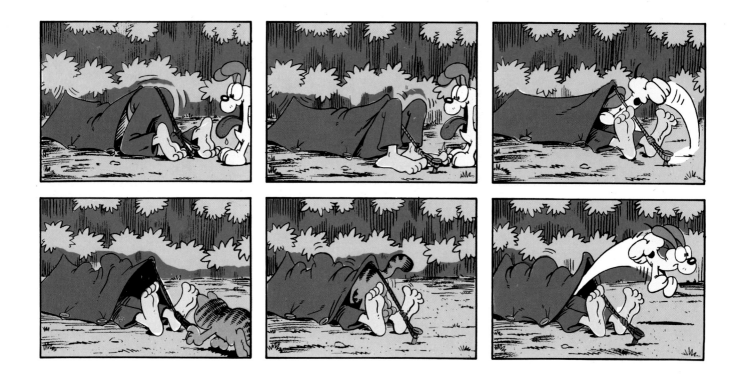

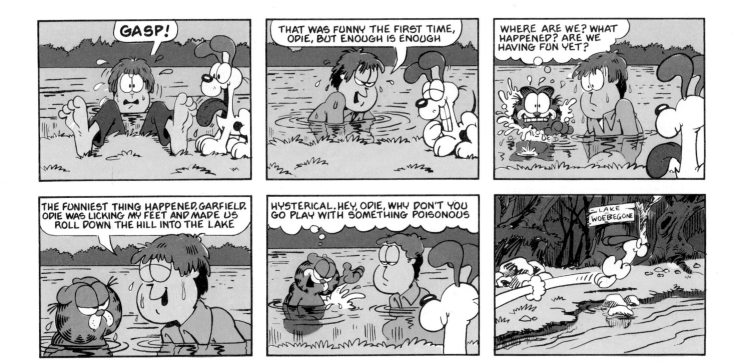

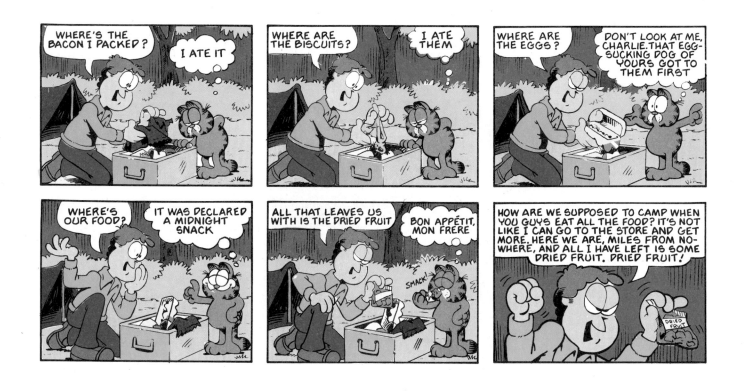

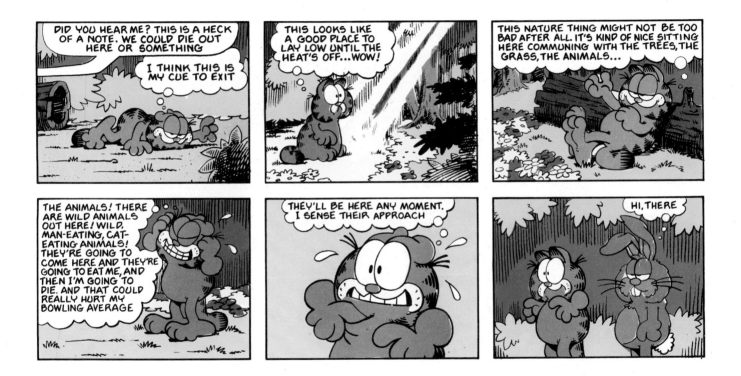

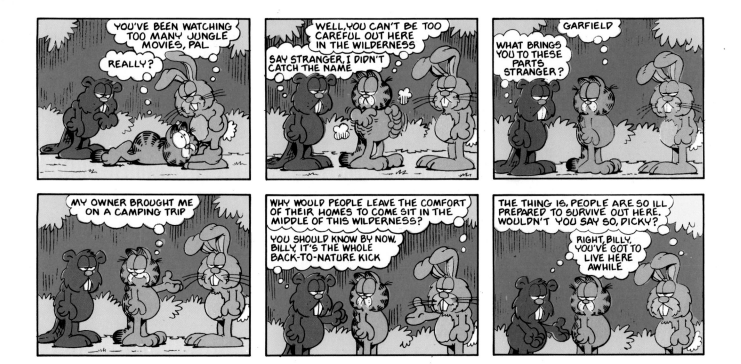

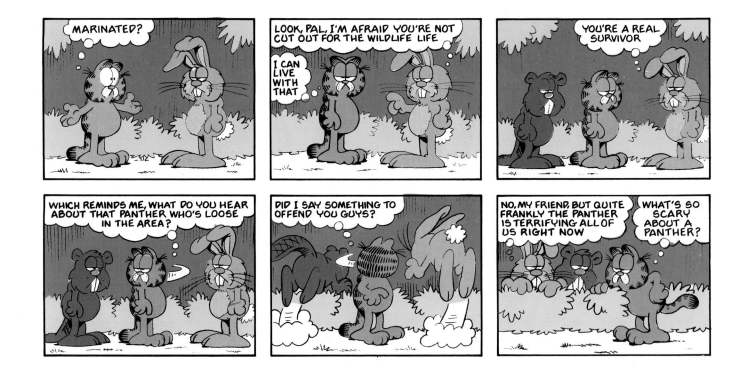

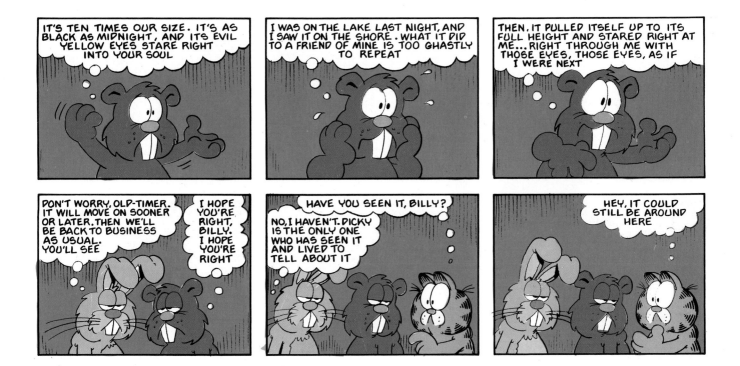

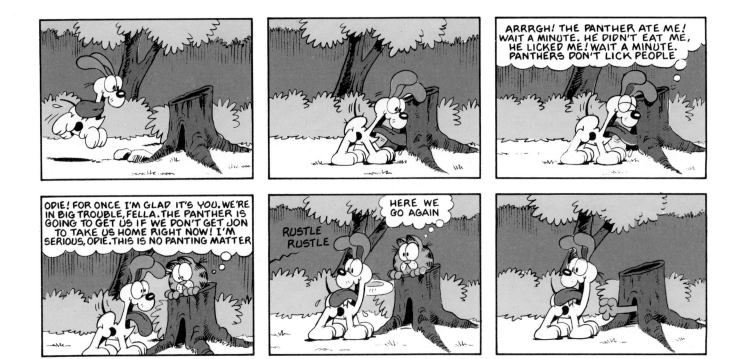

RRRRRR

SLASH!

COME ON, ODIE. IT'LL BE SAFER IN THE CAR! WHERE'S GARFIELD? COME ON, BOY, GET IN!

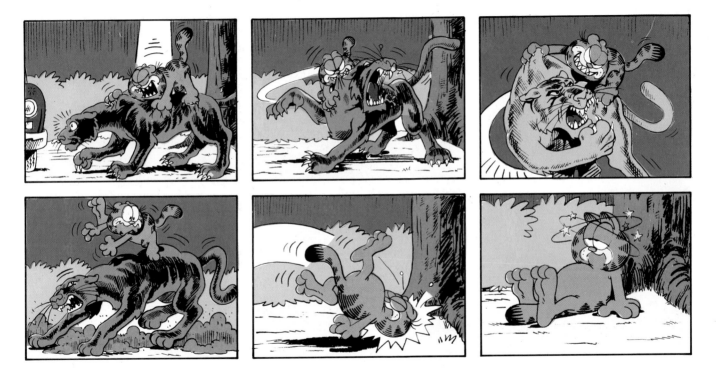

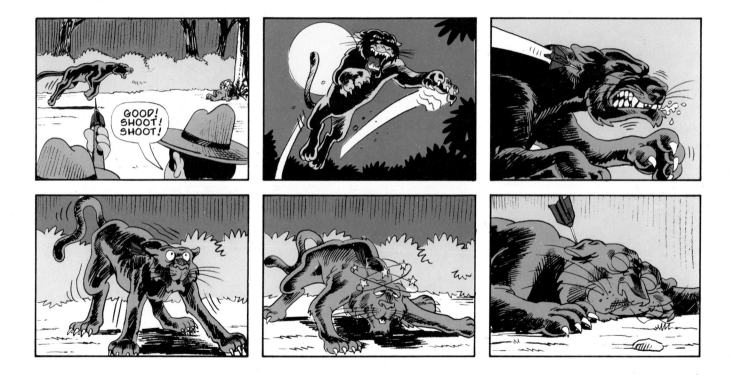

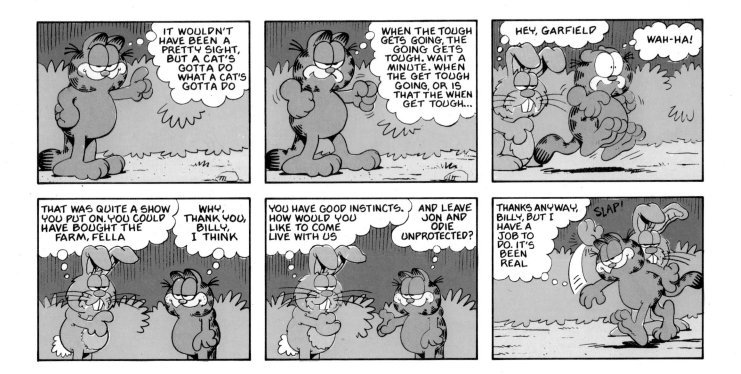

Other Garfield books published by Ravette

Garfield TV Specials

Here Comes Garfield	£2.95
Garfield On The Town	£2.95
Garfield In Disguise	£2.95
Garfield In Paradise	£2.95

Garfield Landscapes

Garfield The All-Round Sports Star	£2.50
Garfield The Irresistible	£2.50
Garfield On Vacation	£2.50
Garfield Weighs In!	£2.50
Garfield I Hate Monday	£2.50
Garfield Special Delivery	£2.50
Garfield The Incurable Romantic	£2.50

Garfield Pocket books

No. 1	Garfield The Great Lover	£1.50
No. 2	Garfield Why Do You Hate Mondays?	£1.50
No. 3	Garfield Does Pooky Need You?	£1.50
No. 4	Garfield Admit It, Odie's OK!	£1.50
No. 5	Garfield Two's Company	£1.50
No. 6	Garfield What's Cooking?	£1.50
No. 7	Garfield Who's Talking?	£1.50
No. 8	Garfield Strikes Again	£1.50
No. 9	Garfield Here's Looking At You	£1.50
No. 10	Garfield We Love You Too	£1.50
No. 11	Garfield Here We Go Again	£1.50
No. 12	Garfield Life and Lasagne	£1.50

All these books are available at your local bookshop or newsagent, or can be ordered direct from the publisher. Just tick the titles you require and fill in the form below. Prices and availability subject to change without notice.

Ravette Limited, 3 Glenside Estate, Star Road, Partridge Green, Horsham, West Sussex RH13 8RA

Please send a cheque or postal order and allow the following for postage and packing. UK: Pocket books and TV Specials – 45p for one book plus 20p for the second book and 15p for each additional book. Landscape Series – 45p for one book plus 30p for each additional book.

Name ....

Address ....

....